The Little Manual of HAPPINESS

By the same author

★ The Little Manual of Success
★ The Little Manual of Meditation
★ The Little Manual of Enlightenment

The Little Manual of HAPPINESS

7 Simple Steps to a Joyful Life

SoulWords
Vikas Malkani
Best-selling author of
THE LITTLE MANUAL OF SUCCESS

UNICORN BOOKS

This edition published by :
UNICORN BOOKS (P) Ltd., New Delhi-110002
J-3/16 , Daryaganj, New Delhi-110002
☎ 23276539, 23272783, 23272784 • *Fax:* 011-23260518
E-mail: unicornbooks@vsnl.com
Website: www.unicornbooks.in • www.kidscorner.in

Distributors
Pustak Mahal, Delhi
E-mail: info@pustakmahal.com • *Website:* www.pustakmahal.com

ISBN: 978-81-7806-137-5

Editorial and design: Write Media

Original Edition Published by: SoulWords Publishing Pte Ltd., Singapore
www.soulwordspublishing.com

If you want happiness for an hour, take a nap.
If you want happiness for a day, go fishing.
If you want happiness for a year, inherit a fortune.
If you want happiness for a lifetime, help somebody.

A Chinese proverb

This book is dedicated to all the great masters
of the past and present day who have taught us
that happiness is the very purpose of life,
and how to live in it in every moment.

Happiness is Now, or Never!
This is the moment for happiness;
Seize it.

Contents

Author's Note

The pursuit of happiness—or the pursuit of 'happyness' as a popular movie spells it—is what motivates all of us. We want to be happy and we spend our waking hours working towards the fulfilment of this goal.

Beneath our so-called wants and desires for love, comfort, wealth, power, fame and much more, lies the unchanging quality of happiness that all of us, without exception, seek—some consciously and most unconsciously. It is, however, imperative to recognise that there is no one absolute way to arrive at happiness. There is no one path, no one science and no eternal unchangeable laws. There are, fortunately, hints and guidelines that can be followed, to hasten our journey and to make it smoother and less painful.

Happiness is essentially a product of a certain inner consciousness, which perceives everything in the externally manifested world. It is to make your journey to this happiness or inner consciousness easier that these practical hints and suggestions, the seven steps to a joyful life, are presented in this little manual. They may be disarming in their simplicity, but if you accept them and absorb them into your inner consciousness, and put them into action, you shall be pleasantly surprised by their inherent power to transform your entire life.

So go ahead, read them and make them a part of your life. Be happy!

Vikas Malkani

| Chapter One |

Choose Happiness

Most people are about as happy as they make up their minds to be.

Abraham Lincoln

It is not what happens to us in life that determines our happiness so much as the way we react to what happens. It is our perception, our point of view, which makes us happy or unhappy.

On just having lost his job, David may decide that he now has the opportunity to have a new work experience, to explore some exciting possibilities and to exercise his independence in the workplace. Whereas his brother Robert may, under the same circumstances, decide to jump off a twenty-storey building and end it all. Given the same situation, one man rejoices while the other commits suicide. One man sees disaster and the other sees opportunity.

I may have simplified things a little here, but the fact remains that we decide on how we react in life and even if we lose control, that is a decision that we make. *We* choose to be happy or not. It all springs from the inner recesses of our mind.

Being happy is not always easy, though. It can be one of the greatest challenges that we face and can sometimes take all the determination, persistence and self-discipline that we can muster. Maturity means taking responsibility for our own happiness and choosing to concentrate on what we have got rather than on what we do not have.

We are necessarily in control of our own happiness as only we decide the thoughts we think. No one else puts thoughts in our mind. To be happy, we need to concentrate on happy thoughts. How often, though, do we do the opposite? How often do we ignore the compliments that are paid to us yet dwell on unkind words for weeks afterwards? If you allow a bad experience or a nasty remark to occupy your mind, it is you who will suffer the consequences.

★ We choose our own state of mind, our happiness or unhappiness ★

I remember, when I was about twenty-five years old, I asked myself, "If you are going to be a really happy person some day, why don't you start now?" That day I decided to be a whole lot happier than I had ever been before. I was stunned. It actually worked! I then began to ask other happy people how they came to be so happy. Invariably, their answer reflected my own experience. They would say, "I had enough misery, heartache, loneliness and finally I decided to change things."

Living in this high tech-low touch world distances us from our peaceful core in more ways than we realise. Before we know it, we have unconsciously taken on a career we don't like and burdens we would rather not have. We even accumulate massive debt by attempting to fill the emptiness within us with the latest and most expensive material possessions.

Whether we are business professionals mastering the corporate world or housewives managing a household, the amazing fact is that we have collected all this stress upon ourselves rather unconsciously. We choose our own state of mind, our happiness or unhappiness. And often, we don't choose deliberately. We are now living the fast life, only it's not the one we chose.

How do We Change?

Awareness is the practice of staying awake moment to moment; to be fully present and available to every moment; to choose deliberately. Creating this state of awareness is the first step towards becoming happy and living a life of freedom. The more aware you become, the greater your control over your life grows, and vice versa.

Your awareness in the moment can transform each challenging life moment and situation into a new beginning for you. Practising awareness leads to authentic inner change, and this is synonymous with being in charge of your own happiness, freedom and destiny. Remember that as you increase your state of awareness, you attract to yourself higher events and opportunities. As the ancient Masters and scriptures of all cultures remind us constantly, there really is no such thing as a wasted step when your final destination is self-transformation.

Here are a few practical ways that will help you reclaim your happiness and freedom.

Step 1: *Stop the rat race; find your life*

Freedom and happiness cannot come where a mad race is being run after a seemingly elusive goal. Dare to slow down your life and step out of the rush to do more and more, possess more and more. No matter how fast your thoughts and desires run, finally they take you nowhere. To find the timeless, dare to step out of the daily grind, and live as though you have all the time in the world at your command and can truly decide how to use it.

> ★ Awareness is the practice of staying awake moment to moment; to be fully present and available to every moment; to choose deliberately ★

Step 2: *Accept responsibility of your life-experience and everything in it*

Whatever you experience in your life, that is, whatever happens in your life, and the way you feel and react towards it, is a direct expression of who you are. At the deepest level, everything occurring in your life-experience is the result of your own desires, choices, actions and reactions. Accept full responsibility. Exercise control over what your life is now and what you want it to be. Resolve that just for today you will not get angry, not worry, and will remember to count your blessings, no matter *what* life brings.

Step 3: *Release all resentments and blame*

If you truly accept responsibility for your life, you spontaneously release all blame and resentments. It's important for you to see that holding on to some hurt or hatred over what others may have done in the past makes you their slave in the 'here and now'.

Step 4: *Refuse to have a short-term vision*

Simply drop any desire, thought or action that promises short-term, temporary or instant gratification at the expense of a more permanent conflict or disharmony. Choose to be whole. Begin by consciously refusing to compromise yourself.

Step 5: *Choose insecurity*

Anyone in life can do what everyone else does, which is nothing 'extra-ordinary'. Do more than you think you can; take the step you think you can't.

Dare to leave security and comfort behind. The limits you have known are the ones you are secure and comfortable with. The ones you still have to explore are the ones that make you insecure and uncomfortable.

See this. Then start going beyond your known self.

Step 6: *Resign as the judge*

The easiest and most unconscious thing to do is to walk around judging every moment, event and person who comes into your life-experience. Remember that even when you judge, you do so from your own level of awareness, and if you want to raise that, you must turn your attention to yourself, inwards, not outwards towards others.

Step 7: *Lighten up*

The heart feels heavy when each and every thought and emotion is taken seriously, as a permanent reality. Remember that your true nature is neither thought nor emotion, rather a pure, free and light spirit. Look at every moment of life through its eyes.

> ★ If you truly accept responsibility for your life, you spontaneously release all blame and resentments ★

Step 8: *Face your own fears*

There is really no such thing as external fear, all of it exists only within you, as a result of one or the other reason. So the next time you start to feel fear, don't look outside you for the reason, look inwards.

It's the inner ground you're standing on that isn't stable. Any fear or weakness faced by looking in this new direction becomes the foundation of a new strength. Fear comes, face it. Fearlessness follows!

Step 9: *Do what is right regardless of consequences*

To choose and do what's right for you, in spite of fearing the consequences that choice may bring, is the same as giving yourself a fearless life. What you are afraid of losing can never be the source of your fearlessness. Do what's right, regardless of the fear or the consequences. All you can finally lose is your fear.

Step 10: *Stop explaining yourself to seek understanding*

The only reason for always ensuring that others are happy with you or for the need to endlessly explain your life to others is that you seek justification of who you are in others' eyes. At a deeper level, this arises from a feeling of insecurity within you.

Step 11: *Follow your passions*

Put what you love first, above all. The rest of your life will take care of itself once you do this because love always finds a way. Love never considers fear. And with love as your guiding light, your success in life is assured because even in work, you have tremendous interest and enjoyment. If you love what you do at all times, how can unhappiness ever enter your life?

The image of the Laughing Buddha comes to mind. He epitomises a happy person who also spreads happiness. Who can look at that stout fellow with his sack and not smile? This leads on to a Zen story that could well explain why he is forever happy. The Laughing Buddha had no inclination to call himself a Zen Master or to have a following. Instead, he was quite content walking about the streets with his sack full of all kinds of goodies. These he would distribute to the children who would gather around him.

Once a Zen Master asked him: "What is the significance of Zen?"

The Laughing Buddha put his sack on the ground.

The Master then asked him: "What is the actualisation of Zen?"

★ Do what's right, regardless of the fear or the consequences. All you can finally lose is your fear ★

The Laughing Buddha, once again, gave no verbal answer. He just smiled, picked up his sack and continued on his path.

Step 1

Choose happiness

A happy person is one who knows that there are options and always chooses the happy one

|Chapter Two|

Be Happy Anyway

Happiness is when what you think, what you say, and what you do are in harmony.

Mahatma Gandhi

If we are unhappy, it is because life is not as we want it. Life is not matching our expectations of how it 'ought' to be and hence we are unhappy. So we begin to say, "I'll be happy when..." Well, life is not perfect. Life is about being exhilarated, frustrated, sometimes achieving and sometimes missing out. As long as we say, "I'll be happy when..." we are deluding ourselves.

Happiness is a decision. Many people live life as if some day they will arrive at 'happiness' like one arrives at a destination. They figure that some day everything will fall into place, that they will take a deep breath and say, "Here I am at last...happy!" Hence their life story is one of "I'll be happy when..."

Each one of us has a decision to make. Are we prepared to remind ourselves daily that we have only limited time to make the most of what we have got, or will we while away the present, hoping for a better future?

As Sri Sri Ravi Shankar puts it, "All of one's life is spent in preparing to be happy some day in the future. It's like making a bed all night, but having no time to sleep. How many minutes, hours and days of our life have we spent being happy from within? Those are the only moments you have really lived life."

How many of us are busy making beds the whole night through? And how many of us are actually enjoying a good night's sleep? Happiness does not depend on your tomorrow; happiness is today, the present moment. Happiness is also being at peace with whatever comes your way. A joyous person knows no ups and downs; for him or her life is a river that flows smoothly. He or she learns to give before receiving. He or she also accepts that the simple pleasures of life are what matter.

Happiness does not depend on your tomorrow; happiness is today, the present moment

To go back to the words of Sri Sri Ravi Shankar: "There are two ways of looking at life. One is thinking that 'I'll be happy after achieving a certain objective.' The second is saying, 'I am happy come what may!' Which one do you want to live?"

Are you going to be happy come what may? Are you going to choose happiness above all?

The following piece was written by an eighty-five-year-old man who had learned that he was dying:

"If I had my life to live over again, I'd try to make more mistakes next time. I wouldn't be so perfect. I would relax more. I'd limber up. I'd be sillier than I've been on this trip. In fact, I know very few things that I would take so seriously. I'd be crazier. I'd be less hygienic.

"I'd take more chances, I'd take more trips, I'd climb more mountains, I'd swim more rivers, I'd visit places I've never been to. I'd eat more ice cream and fewer beans.

"I'd have more actual troubles and fewer imaginary ones!

"You see, I was one of those people who lived prophylactically and sensibly and sanely hour after hour and day after day. Oh, I've had my moments, and if I had to do over again, I'd have more of those moments—moment by moment by moment.

"I've been one of those people who never went anywhere without a thermometer, a hot water bottle, a gargle, a raincoat and a parachute. If I had to do all over again, I'd travel lighter next time. If I had it to do all over again, I'd start barefoot earlier in the spring and stay way later in the fall. I'd ride more merry-go-rounds, I'd watch more sunrises, and I'd play with more children, if I have my life to live over again.

"But you see, I don't."

Isn't this message a beautiful reminder? The old man realised that in order to be happier, in order to get more out of life, he did not have to go and change the world. The world is already beautiful. He only had to change himself.

Happiness lies within us; we have to be ready for it. We should also be prepared to make minor adjustments along the way

This is something we all have to realise. Happiness lies within us; we have to be ready for it. We should also be prepared to make minor adjustments along the way to ensure that we do arrive at the state of happiness.

According to an old Hindu legend, there was a time when all men were happy, but they misused happiness. Brahma the Creator decided to take it away and hide it where no one could possibly find it. There were many suggestions—bury it deep in the earth, sink it into the ocean—but it appeared there was no place that man could not reach. Lord Brahma's decision: "We will hide it deep down in man himself, for he will never think to look for it there."

And since then man goes looking for happiness in all unlikely places, circumstances or people, neglecting to look within.

There is no textbook formula for 'happiness'. There is also no way of determining who or which country is the happiest of them all. There have been several studies to this end. Going by its own set of benchmarks, the University of Leicester rated Denmark as the happiest country. Bhutan has a Gross Happiness Index that defines prosperity not merely in terms of economic growth but also bases it on the average level of the happiness of its inhabitants. And a recent University of Warwick study has revealed that there is a correlation between happiness and the level of blood pressure.

To my mind, happiness does not need to be quantified. It just is.

Realise that the world is not perfect. The degree of our unhappiness is the distance between the way things are in reality and the way we think they 'ought' to be. If we cease to demand things to be perfect, the business of being happy becomes easier.

We will then choose to have preferences for the way things might be, and decide that if our preferences are not met, we will be happy anyway. Writes Dr Wayne W. Dyer: "If you believe in happiness and abundance, think only about them, talk about them with others, and act on your belief in them, it is a very good bet that you are seeing what you believe."

As an Indian guru once told a pupil who was in desperate search of contentment, "I will give you the secret. If you want to be happy, BE HAPPY!" Choose happiness; accept that there is joy in imperfection.

You are Perfectly Imperfect Right this Minute

You always have been perfectly imperfect, you always will be. You will make mistakes on occasions, do things you wish you had not done, long for things you do not have. You are capable of honesty and sneakiness, kindness and hatred, compassion and cruelty. At the same time, however, you are a perfect living being, you have been entrusted with a life that is yours, to care for, enjoy and learn from. There is no one just like you. There never will be.

★ If we cease to demand things to be perfect, the business of being happy becomes easier ★

Many people have an unrealistic notion of what it means to be human. People talk about "having it all together", which is an illusory notion because we are always in a state of change.

They think a day will come when they will no longer misplace their keys, lose their temper, offend other people, get sacred, or feel at a loss for words. They may also think they will be able to stick to a diet, have a stimulating job that pays well, be liked by everyone, and wake up every day feeling bright and alert. If you really think these things are possible, look around you. Does anyone fit this description?

If you want to be happy, kiss these thoughts goodbye. When they come into your mind, smile at them without taking them seriously.

Remember, just because your head is full of the plentiful 'shoulds', which gobble up your self-esteem, does not make them true.

Perfection is in truth, honesty and kindness as we walk our path. The goal is not to avoid slipping off the path, but to slide off with grace. Be kind to yourself. Often, our pursuit of perfection overshadows our pursuit of happiness. When this happens, expect disaster.

I define a perfectionist as not someone who does things perfectly; rather, someone who is perfectly happy.

Let me introduce Ben-Shahar to you. He is a former Israeli soldier and a squash champion. Ostensibly, he had it all. Success in the classroom as well as in the playing field, he had plenty of friends and the future looked bright. Then why was he not happy?

An undergraduate at Harvard, Ben decided to turn to positive psychology to find the answer to his dilemma. Today, he is working on two books and confesses that he is a much happier man. Here are his lessons in happiness that are relevant here:

Lesson 1: *Give yourself permission to be human. When we accept emotions as natural, we are more likely to overcome them.*
This lesson also gels well with the concept of de-linking happiness and perfection.

Lesson 2: *Happiness lies at the intersection between pleasure and meaning. Whether at work or at home, the goal is to engage in activities that are both personally significant and enjoyable.*
Learn to find the 'middle path' and you will always be happy.

Often, our pursuit of perfection overshadows our pursuit of happiness. When this happens, expect disaster

Lesson 3: *Keep in mind that happiness is mostly dependent on our state of mind, not on our status or the state of our bank account.*
Never, ever, equate happiness with anything material. That is a shortcut to misery.

Lesson 4: *Simplify! We are, generally, too busy, trying to squeeze in more and more activities into less and less time.*
This is something I have always believed in. Get rid of all the extra baggage, the clutter that occupies our mental and physical space, and watch joy expanding to fit in the emptiness.

Lesson 5: *Remember the mind-body connection. What we do or don't do with our bodies influences our mind.*
Back to the body-mind continuum. Never neglect one for the other. A happy person is happy in and out. Both the inner and outer selves should resonate with joy.

Lesson 6: *Express gratitude, whenever possible. We too often take our lives for granted.*

What can I add to this, save, perhaps, a big 'thank you' to Ben and to all my readers!

Don't Sweat the Small Stuff

Here again, I am going to turn to an expert on the subject: Richard Carlson, the best-selling author of the amazing *Don't Sweat the Small Stuff* series and, of course, *What about the Big Stuff*? When Richard's daughter Jazzy was a little girl, she used to tell her friends that her dad teaches people to be happy. That indeed is what Richard does with his words. An excerpt: "I once heard Rabbi Harold Kushner on the radio. He said something to the effect that 'people are so busy chasing happiness—if they would slow down and turn around, they would give it a chance to catch up with them'. Happiness is within the grasp of anyone. One of the keys, however, is to stop grasping. Happiness is a state of mind, not a set of circumstances."

So stop letting life's problems—the big and the small stuff both—get in your way. Make happiness your path instead of your destination and watch how beautiful life appears. Often we allow ourselves to get worked up about things that, upon closer examination, are not really that big a deal. We focus on little problems and concerns and blow them way out of proportion. A stranger, for example, might cut in front of us in traffic. Rather than let it go, and carry on with our day, we convince ourselves that we are justified in our anger. We play out an imaginary confrontation in our mind. Many of us might even tell someone else about the incident later, rather than simply let it go. Try to have compassion for the person and remember how painful it is to be in such an enormous hurry. In this way, we can maintain our own sense of well-being and also avoid taking other people's problems and worries personally.

★ Happiness is within the grasp of anyone. One of the keys, however, is to stop grasping ★

There are many similar, 'small stuff' examples that occur every day in our lives. Whether we have to wait in line, listen to unfair criticism, or do the lion's share of the work, it pays enormous dividends if we learn not to worry about little things. So many people spend so much of their life's energy 'sweating the small stuff' that they completely lose touch with the magic and beauty of life. When you commit to working towards being happy, you will find that you will have far more energy to be kinder and gentler. Leave your worries and troubles behind; look ahead with optimism. Look for the rainbows instead of the ditches; the butterflies instead of the demons.

Step 2

Be happy anyway

A contented person is happy no matter how things are

|Chapter Three|

Make Peace with Imperfection

Happiness makes up for in height what it lacks in length.

Robert Frost

I have yet to meet an absolute perfectionist whose life is filled with inner peace. The need for perfection and the desire for inner tranquillity conflict with each other. Whenever we are attached to having something a certain way, better than it already is, we are, almost by definition, engaged in a losing battle. Rather than being content and grateful for what we have, we are focussed on what is wrong with something and our need to fix it. When we are zeroed in on what is wrong, it implies that we are dissatisfied, discontented.

Whether it is related to ourselves—a disorganised closet, a scratch on the car, an imperfect accomplishment, a few pounds we would like to lose—or to someone else's 'imperfections'—the way someone looks, behaves, or lives one's life—the very act of focussing on imperfection pulls us away from our desire of being happy and gentle. This strategy has nothing to do with ceasing to do your very best but with being overly attached and focussed on what is wrong with life. It is about realising that while there is always a better way to do something, this does not mean that you cannot enjoy and appreciate the way things already are.

The solution here is to catch yourself when you fall into your habit of insisting that things should be other than what they are. Gently remind yourself that life is okay the way it is, right now. In the absence of your judgement, everything would be fine. As you begin to eliminate your need for perfection in all areas of your life, you will begin to discover the perfection in life itself. And yes, that is bound to bring happiness into your life.

★ As you begin to eliminate your need for perfection in all areas of your life, you will begin to discover the perfection in life itself ★

Let me give you ten suggestions on how to maintain a state of happiness and joy-full-ness as you sail your ship in this ocean of life. Remember, we live in two worlds simultaneously, the inner and the outer worlds. To become joyful and experience happiness as an apparent quality in our daily life it is necessary that we maintain awareness of both these worlds in every moment. The steps below are intended to keep you firmly on the path of freedom and happiness in every moment of every day. Practise, and be happy—all-ways, always!

Step 1: *Laugh at failure and defeat*

Defeat and failure are only a perception from a small vision. They have no real life of their own except what you give them. This means that the only time you have to feel the pain of any defeat or failure is if you ask for it, by delving into troubled thoughts about some painful past loss. Stay in the present moment. Consciousness likes great heights; dare to follow!

Step 2: *Start all over again, if necessary*

Any time you truly choose, you can start your life over, without permission from any higher authority. You can have just as many new beginnings as you are willing to leave behind all your old ideas and conditioning about the concepts of right and wrong.

Life can be as new as you choose it to be.

Step 3: *Stop looking outside of yourself*

After endlessly looking for it outside, realise that the answer is within you. Your life is only as complete as you are—no more, no less. Looking to your work, relationships or events for a feeling of self-completion is a self-defeating exercise.

Being complete and whole is first an understanding, and then a state of being. It does not need a certain set of conditions to be perfectly manifested for its occurrence.

Step 4: *Let go*

Trying to control every moment of your life, or another's, causes more disharmony than any other process. Keep in mind that everything and every person must go through their own lives, based on their own awareness, at their own pace. Allow this to happen.

Let something higher have its hand at directing your life, in shaping your destiny. Learn to let go!

Step 5: *Don't live for others*

There is no satisfying the fear that you may displease others. Allowing what others may feel about you to dictate how you feel about yourself is like believing that someone else can decide your identity for you. This choice gives away your power. The only real strength comes from knowing that you have your own likes and dislikes in your own life, and can never make everyone happy with everything that you are, or can do.

> After endlessly looking for it outside, realise that the answer is within you. Your life is only as complete as you are—no more, no less

Step 6: *Believe in action*

Wisdom turns into strength only if it is followed up with action. To learn how to swim, you must be prepared to get wet. Any weakness voluntarily faced and met is the same as greeting a greater strength.

Wisdom lays the foundation, but it is action that finally changes life and the future.

Step 7: *Be optimistic*

You always have two choices in every situation—either curse the darkness, or light a candle. Choose the more positive attitude, always, regardless of the situation. It comes at the same expense as the negative thought or choice but with extremely different consequences.

Why wait until you feel down before you think of looking up. You can always glimpse the higher, in every moment, but you have to remind yourself to look in the right direction. Remember that if you keep your face to the sunshine, you cannot see the shadows.

Step 8: *Choose the heart over the head*

No matter how much you try, you can't think yourself into happiness. You must actually feel happy. However, you can sink yourself to your lowest low with a chain of thoughts that start from a single dark one.

Bright, positive emotions spring from the heart. Heavy feelings can't exist without the presence of negative thoughts. This means that sad states are just a trick of the mind, and begin with our thoughts.

Step 9: *Walk one step at a time*

Don't be too concerned about how much there is to do, or how impossible some of the tasks seem. Just get one thing done at a time, again and again. Just do what's in your power, and brush aside all other concerns. The journey of a thousand miles begins with a single step. And the most beautiful tapestry begins and ends with one of ten thousand individual threads.

Step 10: *Know that the time to act is always 'now'*

You can't change the mind of the person you are later. There is no later, it's always now or never. The moment, ever present, ever powerful, is before you. And it has limitless potential. The time to accept responsibility for your happiness and freedom is now. The time to change your destiny is *now*. Accept that change is inevitable; it is part of our life's journey. Confucius wisely said, "They must often change who would be constant in happiness or wisdom."

★ Remember that if you keep your face to the sunshine, you cannot see the shadows ★

Be ready to accommodate change in your life. Your personal growth depends on this. So does your state of mind. Do not delay. I have always maintained that there is really never a better time than the present. More about this in the next chapter.

Step 3

Accept imperfection

You don't have to wait for perfection to be happy

|Chapter Four|

Live Your Life Now

Happiness does not consist in having what you want, but in wanting what you have.

Confucius

Do not put off living your life until you are 'better'. That is probably just the latest in a series of perfect reasons why you have not fully lived up until this moment. ("I'll do it when I'm older." "I'll do it when I've learned more." "I'll do it when I find my soulmate." "I'll do it when I have the time." "I'll do it when…")

Regarding all those things you have put off until 'later', keep this in mind: you are in your 'laters' now.

Start doing the things you have always wanted to do and enjoy each moment by finding something enjoyable, now.

We are not talking about executing every grand scheme your imagination has ever created such as: "I've always wanted to be ruler of the world." We are talking about overcoming the tendency to say, "When my life is better, then I'll be able to start focussing on positive things."

We often form a habit of procrastination. Yes, we put off unpleasant activities, but we also tend to put off the enjoyable ones. We dole out pleasure, contentment and happiness as though they were somehow rationed. The supply of these things is limitless (as, by the way, is the supply of misery, pain and suffering). We tend to do the rationing ourselves.

★ Start doing the things you have always wanted to do and enjoy each moment by finding something enjoyable, now ★

If you look, you'll find all the perfect reasons why you should not enjoy your life, why you should postpone enjoyment until certain things are different.

Understand that the only thing that has to be different for you to enjoy your life is where you focus your attention.

In life we have either reasons or results. If we do not have what we want (results), we usually have a long list of reasonable reasons for why we do not have the results. We tend to rationalise (pronounced 'rational lies'). All this is a waste of energy and a convincing argument that we cannot have what we want, which becomes another reason not to live.

When you do not get what you want, rather than wasting time and energy explaining why you do not have it, find another way to get it. Focus your attention and look for all the positive things taking place in and around you right now. If you cannot find something positive about your environment, look again with 'fresh eyes'. Try another point of view. Be creative. What good are you taking for granted? If you cannot find anything, hold your breath. Within a few minutes, you will really appreciate breathing.

Whatever Anyone Says or Does Means Nothing about Your Worth

A great deal of my work centres on helping people realise that other people's opinions of them are simply opinions that come through their own filter. In other words, whatever anyone says or does means nothing, absolutely nothing, about your worth as a human being.

A person may give you useful feedback, have something valuable to say, but whether they like you, approve of you, or admire you, need not affect your sense of worth or self-esteem. If everyone could internalise this belief, we could all relax and enjoy the show—the snow, the rain, the great big picture of life. We are free to feel joy when our self-worth rests quietly within us, not on the lips of others.

Unfortunately, many people live as if their self-esteem had a cord connecting them to external events and people. You receive praises, someone says you are nice or sends you a Valentine's Day card and your self-esteem goes up. You do not pass your driving test, you get fired, someone is rude to you, your best friend forgets your birthday and your self-esteem goes down. This is the essence of a victim stance; you think the world is doing it to you. While you may have been victimised in your life, you are not a victim until you agree to be. You have a mind that can operate on your behalf by saying over and over: "Whatever anyone says means nothing about my worth."

Stop worrying about what everyone thinks about you because, usually, they are not thinking about you at all; instead, they may well be wondering what you are thinking of them

An analogy that is sometimes useful is imagining that someone throws a dart at your arm. It cuts your skin, you bleed, and it stings. But you always have a choice about what you can say to your heart and soul. You can hurt yourself further by saying: "He threw a dart at me. What did I do to deserve this? What did I do wrong? I must be a jerk and a bad person." Or you can also be kind to yourself by saying: "Ouch, that person threw a dart, that's not nice, that hurts. I'd better get out of here and get a bandage and stay away from people who throw darts."

Stop worrying about what everyone thinks about you because, usually, they are not thinking about you at all; instead, they may well be wondering what you are thinking of them. What I am trying to highlight here is the simple fact that externals (people, events) should not affect you and destroy your mental balance. You have to learn to live in the moment and be happy now. After all, you chose happiness in an earlier chapter!

Your Worth

Imagine that you were in charge of the care of a three-month-old baby. At feeding time, would you feed the baby with no strings attached? Of course you would! You will not say, "Okay kid! Unless you can do something smart or witty, unless you can sit up and say your ABC or make me laugh, you don't get a drink!"

You feed the baby because it deserves to be fed. It needs love, care and fair treatment. It deserves all that because, like you, it is a human being, a part of the universe.

You deserve exactly the same. You deserved it when you were born and you deserve it *now*.

Too many people get the idea that unless they are as clever, smart, handsome, highly paid, sporty, witty as other people they know, they are undeserving of love and respect.

Pause for a minute and reflect on this sentence: You deserve love and respect just because you are *you*.

Too rarely do most of us focus on our real inner beauty and our inner strengths. Do you recall watching 'boy meets girl' movies? As the boy and girl struggled through thick and thin, you hoped and prayed the whole time that everything would work out. He went to war, she left home, he came back, she was gone, he found her, her brother told him to get lost, she told him to get lost, and all the time you hoped that they would live happily ever after. They were married and strolled off into the sunset as the curtain came down. You dried your tears and, clutching your empty popcorn packet, strolled out of the theatre.

★ Pause for a minute and reflect on this sentence: You deserve love and respect just because you are *you* ★

We cry at those movies because, at our deepest level, we care. We love. We hurt. There is that inner core in all of us that is simply beautiful.

Depending on how much we have been hurt, we will expose our deepest feelings, but we all share these qualities.

When we see the news stories that portray the plight of people starving around the globe, we all ache inside for them. Each of us may have a different view as to how they can best be helped, but we all care. That is the way we are.

Accept that you have these qualities—the capacity to love and empathise and be human as you are human. Recognise your own worth and constantly remind yourself that you deserve to be treated well.

I have found that a happy person is one who has realised his or her worth. When you think you are great, others will too.

Poor Self-image Behaviour

Each of us must work continually on maintaining a positive and healthy self-image. The following behaviour traits are evidence that there is considerable room for improvement in our self-image:

- Negative talk about ourselves
- Experiencing guilt
- Failure to pay compliments
- Non-acceptance of compliments
- Not taking our own needs into account
- Not asking for what we want
- Starving ourselves of luxuries unnecessarily
- Failure to give affection
- Inability to receive and enjoy affection
- Criticism of others
- Comparison of ourselves with others
- Constant poor health

Change is difficult. The action of a poor self-image is always to perpetuate itself. As we start out on the road to self-improvement, the tendency is to keep replaying the old patterns of blame, guilt and self-denigration.

Here are some suggestions for things that you can do to boost the way you feel about yourself:

- Accept compliments. Always say 'thank you' or words to that effect.

- Pay compliments. One of the easiest ways to feel good about ourselves is to recognise the beauty in others.

- Always speak well of yourself. If you have nothing good to say about yourself, keep quiet.

One of the easiest ways to feel good about ourselves is to recognise the beauty in others

- Praise yourself. When you do something right, give yourself a pat on the back. Acknowledge your value.

- Separate your behaviour from yourself. Realise that your behaviour is not connected to your self-worth. If you do something silly, like smash into another person's car, it does not make you a bad person. You simply made a mistake. It is best to love the sinner and hate the sin.

- Treat your body well—it is the only one you have got. Everything we do affects everything else. Exercise and nourish it well.

- Let people know how you expect to be treated—in particular, set an example by the way you treat yourself and them. Nobody should accept abuse from anybody.

- Get around good people. They will, inevitably, have a positive effect on your way of thinking.

- Work at having pleasure without guilt. Life is too short; enjoy the journey. God did not want us to be martyrs, there is just no harm in having fun, as long as it is not at the expense of someone else.

- Use affirmations. This works, try it.

- Read books that give you ideas and inspiration. Note down stuff that you particularly enjoyed and refer to them often, especially when you need a quick pick-me-up.

- Always picture in your mind how you want to be, not how you are. You will then necessarily gravitate towards your dominant thoughts.

Understand Separate Realities

While we are on the subject of being interested in the way other people do things, let us take a moment to discuss separate realities.

If you have travelled to foreign countries or seen depictions of them in movies, you are aware of the vast differences among cultures. The principle of separate realities says that the difference among individuals is every bit as vast. Just as we would not expect people of different cultures to see or do things as we would (in fact, we would be disappointed if they did), this principle tells us that the individual differences in our ways of seeing the world prohibit this as well.

It is not a matter of merely tolerating all differences but also of truly understanding and honouring the fact that it literally cannot be any other way. I have seen that an understanding of this simple principle changes lives and spreads happiness all round. It can virtually eliminate quarrels. When we expect to see things differently, when we take for granted that others will do things differently and react differently to the same stimuli, the compassion we have for ourselves, and for others, rises dramatically. The moment we expect otherwise, the potential for conflict exists.

The world will be a happier place for all of us if we reach out to our brothers and sisters in the spirit of one

The Dalai Lama tells us: "If you want others to be happy, practise compassion. If you want to be happy, practise compassion." That, in essence, is the meaning of happiness.

When you care for others, when you see the oneness in all humanity, you will learn to be truly happy. And, of course, the world will be a happier place for all of us if we reach out to our brothers and sisters in the spirit of one. You may well counter that we are all different individuals, with different likes and dislikes, with different habits and tastes. I encourage you to consider deeply and respect the fact that we are all very different. For when you do this, the love you feel for others, as well as the appreciation you have for your own uniqueness, will increase manifold.

Become More Patient

The quality of patience goes a long way towards your goal of creating a more peaceful and loving self. The more patient you are, the more accepting you will be of what you have, rather than insisting that life be exactly as you would like it to be. Without patience, life is extremely frustrating. You are easily annoyed, bothered and irritated. Patience adds a dimension of ease and acceptance to your life. It is essential for inner peace.

Becoming more patient involves opening your heart to the present moment, even if you do not like it. If you were stuck in a traffic jam or late for an appointment, opening to the moment would mean catching yourself building a mental snowball, before your thinking got out of hand, and gently reminding yourself to relax. It might be a good time to inhale and exhale slowly.

This is also a good opportunity to remind yourself that, in the bigger scheme of things, being late is 'small stuff'. Patience involves seeing the innocence in others. When I remember to see the innocence, it immediately brings forth a feeling of patience, and my attention is at once brought back to the present moment.

I have found that, if you look deeply enough, you can almost always see the innocence in other people as well as in potentially frustrating situations. When you do, you will become a more patient and peaceful person and, in some strange way, you begin to enjoy many of the moments that used to earlier frustrate you.

Be the First One to Act Loving or to Reach Out

So many of us hold on to little resentments that may have stemmed from an argument, a misunderstanding, the way we were raised, or some other painful event. Stubbornly, we wait for someone else to reach out to us, believing this is the only way we can forgive or rekindle a friendship or family relationship.

> ★ If you look deeply enough, you can almost always see the innocence in other people as well as in potentially frustrating situations ★

Whenever we hold on to our anger, we turn 'small stuff' into really 'big stuff' in our minds. We start to believe that our positions are more important than our happiness. They are not. If you want to be a more peaceful person you must understand that being right is almost never more important than allowing yourself to be happy.

The way to be happy is to let go, and reach out. Let other people be right. This does not mean that you are wrong. You will experience the peace of letting go, as well as the joy of letting others be right. This will make them less defensive and more loving towards you. They may even reach back.

But, if for some reason they do not, that is okay too. You will be at peace and have the inner satisfaction of knowing that you have done your part to create a more loving world. I am sure that thought alone will bring much joy.

Become a Better Listener

Effective listening is more than simply avoiding the bad habit of interrupting others while they are speaking or finishing their sentences. It also means to be content listening to the entire thought of someone rather than waiting impatiently for your chance to respond.

In some ways, the way we fail to listen is symbolic of the way we live. We often treat communication as if it were a race. It is almost as if our goal is to have no time gaps between the conclusion of the sentence of the person we are speaking with and the beginning of our own.

Slowing down your responses and becoming a better listener aids you in becoming a more peaceful person. It takes pressure away from you. If you think about it, you will notice that it takes an enormous amount of energy and is very stressful to be sitting at the edge of your seat trying to guess what the person in front of you (or on the telephone) is going to say so that you can fire back your response.

But as you wait for the people you are communicating with to finish, to simply listen more intently to what is being said, you will immediately feel more relaxed, and so will the people you are talking to. They will also feel safe in slowing down their own responses because they will not feel themselves in competition with you. This will help enhance the quality of your relationships with them.

Sometimes people need to be pushed to the brink before they realise that this life belongs to them, not to the demands and desires of others

Everyone loves to talk to someone who truly listens to what they are saying. Often, they do not need your advice; they just need you to listen to them. This makes them happy and, in turn, will make you happy as well.

You Don't Have to Do Anything

Whatever you do, do it because you choose to do it, not from any misguided sense of duty or obligation. Sometimes people need to be pushed to the brink before they realise that this life belongs to them, not to the demands and desires of others. If you have a life-threatening illness, you are on that brink. If you learn that this is your life, you can more easily take a few steps towards de-brinking yourself.

Try saying this in your mind often: "I don't have to do anything." Say it a few times. You will feel the sense of release, of total freedom, of unburdening. You can add to it: "And what I choose to do, I can do."

Together they make a nice (and, perhaps, necessary) affirmation: "I don't have to do anything, and what I choose to do, I can do."

Avoid People and Situations that Upset You

Avoid things, people, situations and experiences you are averse to. Some might call this cowardly; I call it smart. The world is brimming with things, people and experiences. We will never experience all of them. So why not associate with the ones that naturally please you?

In some situations, it becomes difficult to reach a person (Mr C) you would like to, without passing through others such as Mr A and Mr B. In those cases, keep your eye on Mr C. Keep reminding yourself why you are messing with Mr A and Mr B and that soon you will be at Mr C, and that Mr C will be worth it.

Some examples of things to avoid—parties you do not want to go to, people you do not want to see, television specials you do not want to watch (but think you should), movies everybody else has seen that hold no appeal for you, and so on.

This idea goes contrary to the claim that you grow through confrontation. Yes, this is true. Tribulation and confrontation are great teachers. There is, however, quite enough tribulation presented to you naturally. You do not have to seek it, it will seek you. That is the time to practise acceptance, patience and forbearance. If you can avoid the unpleasantness in the first place, by all means do so. Of course, if you live in the freedom of your own thoughts and desires, you must also give the same freedom to others.

A happy person is one who tries to get rid of *all* negativities. He or she will go the extra mile just to avoid the downbeat and the depressing

Learn to accept the behaviour of others even if it does not fit the pattern of your opinions. Whenever you find yourself disapproving of another, examine your opinions. Explore your list of 'shoulds' and 'should nots'. See your opinion as merely opinion, not truth, and therefore not worth getting upset about.

Others' opinions of you and your opinions of others are the cause of a great deal of unnecessary negative thinking. (I maintain that all negative thinking is unnecessary, but the guilt, fear and resentment generated by opinions are particularly unnecessary.) A happy person is one who tries to get rid of *all* negativities. He or she will go the extra mile just to avoid the downbeat and the depressing.

Accept the fact that we are all different. We come from different backgrounds; our families, our education, our upbringing all stem from diverse areas and thoughts. Be tolerant of these inherent differences. Learn to relish the differences between people. Imagine how dull the world would be if we all thought, spoke and acted the same way. That would indeed be quite boring!

Become Aware of Your Moods

And do not allow yourself to be fooled by the low ones.

Your own moods can be extremely deceptive. They can, and probably do, trick you into believing your life is far worse than it really is. When you are in a good mood, life looks great. In good moods, things do not feel so hard, problems seem less formidable and easier to solve, relationships seem to flow and communication is easy. If you are criticised, you take it in your stride.

On the contrary, when you are in a bad mood, life looks unbearably serious and difficult, you have very little perspective. You take things personally and often tend to misinterpret those around you, as you impute malignant motives to their actions.

Here is the catch: People do not realise that their moods are always on the run. They think instead that their lives have suddenly become worse in the past day, or even the last hour. So, someone who is in a good mood in the morning might love his wife, his job and his car. He is probably optimistic about his future and feels grateful about his past. But by late afternoon, if his mood is bad, he claims he hates his job, thinks of his wife as a nuisance and believes he is going nowhere in his career. If you ask him about his childhood while he is trapped in a low mood, he will probably blame his parents for his current plight.

A low mood is not the best time to analyse your life. To do so is emotional suicide

Such quick and drastic contrasts may seem absurd, even funny, but we are all like that. In low moods we lose our perspectives and everything seems urgent. We completely forget that when we are in a good mood. We experience the identical circumstances—who we are married to, where we work, the car we drive, our potential, our childhood—entirely differently, depending on our mood at that moment.

When we are low, rather than blaming our mood as would be appropriate, we instead tend to feel that our whole life is wrong. It is almost as if we actually believe that our lives have fallen apart in the past hour or two. The truth is, life is almost never as bad as it seems when you are in a low mood.

Rather than staying stuck in a bad temper or an ill mood, learn to question your judgement. Remind yourself, "Of course, I'm feeling defensive [or angry, frustrated, stressed, depressed]; I'm in a bad mood. I always feel negative when I'm low."

When you're in an ill mood, learn to pass it off as an unavoidable human condition that will go with time, if left alone.

A low mood is not the best time to analyse your life. To do so is emotional suicide.

If you have a legitimate problem, it will still be there when your state of mind improves. The trick is to be grateful for our good moods and be graceful in our low moods, not taking them too seriously.

The next time you feel low, for whatever reason, remind yourself, "This too shall pass." It will.

Relax

What does it mean to relax? Despite hearing this term thousands of times during the course of our lives, very few people have deeply considered what it is really about.

When you ask people (which I have done many times) what it means to relax, most will answer in a way that suggests that relaxing is something you plan to do later—you do it on vacation, in a hammock, when you retire, or when you get everything done. This implies, of course, that most other times (the other 95 per cent of your life) should be spent nervous, agitated, rushed and frenzied! Very few actually come out and say so, but this is the obvious implication. For them, relaxation just does not happen.

Could this explain why so many of us operate as if life were one great big emergency? Most of us postpone relaxation until our 'in' basket is empty. Of course it never is. It is useful to think of relaxation as a quality of heart that you can access on a regular basis rather than something reserved for some later time. You can relax *now*.

The next time you feel low, for whatever reason, remind yourself, "This too shall pass." It will

It is helpful to remember that relaxed people can still be super-achievers and, in fact, that relaxation and creativity go hand in hand. When I am feeling uptight, for example, I do not even try to write. But when I feel relaxed, my writing flows quickly and easily.

Being more relaxed involves training yourself to respond differently to the challenges of life. It comes, in part, from reminding yourself over and over again (with loving kindness and patience) that you have a choice in how you respond to life. You can learn to relate to your thinking as well as your circumstances in new ways. With practice, making these choices will translate into a more relaxed self.

Listen to Your Feelings

Be alert, your feelings are trying to tell you something. You have at your disposal a foolproof guidance system to navigate you through life. This system, which consists solely of your own feelings, lets you know whether you are off track and are heading towards unhappiness and conflict; or on track, heading towards peace of mind. Your feelings act as a barometer, letting you know what your internal weather is like.

When you are not caught up in your thinking and taking things too seriously, your feelings will be generally positive. They will be affirming that you are using your thinking to your advantage. No mental adjustment needs to be made.

When your experience of life is other than pleasant and you are feeling angry, resentful, depressed, stressed out, frustrated and so on, your feelings remind you that you are off track, and it is time to ease up on your thinking, as you have lost perspective.

You can think of your negative feelings in the same way you think of the warning lights on the dashboard of your car. When flashing, they let you know that it is time to ease up.

Contrary to popular belief, negative feelings do not need to be studied and analysed. When you analyse these feelings, you will usually end up with more of them to contend with. The next time you are feeling bad, rather than getting stuck in 'analysis paralysis', wondering why you feel the way you do, see, instead, if you can use your feelings to guide you back in the direction towards serenity. Do not pretend that the negative feelings do not exist, but try to recognise the reason why you are taking life so seriously, why you are 'sweating the small stuff'.

Instead of rolling up your sleeves and fighting life, back off, take a few deep breaths and relax.

Remember, life is not an emergency unless you make it so.

Love a Lot

Love is the most important thing in our lives. All the great Masters, saints and sages agree on this. But it seems to me that a lot has been lost in the translation of this teaching. It would appear that many of us have just forgotten how to love, or never learned how to love, to begin with.

Instead of rolling up your sleeves and fighting life, back off, take a few deep breaths and relax. Remember, life is not an emergency unless you make it so

I believe I have learned one thing about love in recent years, which I will share with you.

I have learned that in order to love, we have to love *ourselves* first. We do that by allowing ourselves to do things we love to do. If you are feeling weak in the love department, the first place to start is with yourself. Spend some time figuring out the things you love to do, and the things that make you happy. Then start doing them.

Do not expect things to happen overnight. It may take you a while, and you might need to get some guidance along the way. Fortunately, there is a wealth of information available today to help you do this.

Many times we have been taught that doing what we love to do is selfish or narcissistic. Often we like to appear as 'martyrs', making sure that everyone else is having a great time, at our expense! If you do not love yourself, you will never be able to love another. It is really as simple as that.

The equation works this way: Love for yourself plus love for others equals happiness. There is no shortcut here. You cannot start by loving others and think that, in the process, some of the love will come back to you. No, that is like starting a journey from the destination itself.

Do not even try to go backwards. You need to first come to terms with yourself, be comfortable in your own company, enjoy moments with yourself. Let the love begin at the very source—inside you, in your heart—and then let it go forth into the universe. Before we can give love to others, it is essential that we fill ourselves with love first.

Fill Your Life with Love

I do not know anyone who does not want a life filled with love. For this to happen, the effort must start within us. Rather than waiting for other people to provide the love we desire, we must be a vision and a source of love. We must tap into our own loving kindness in order to set an example for others.

It has been said that "the shortest distance between two points is an intention". This is certainly true with regard to a life filled with love.

★ Before we can give love to others, it is essential that we fill ourselves with love first ★

The starting point or foundation of a life filled with love is the desire and commitment to be a source of love. Our attitude, choices, acts of kindness, and willingness to be the first to reach out, will take us towards this goal.

As Mother Teresa said: "Nothing makes you happier than when you really reach out in mercy to someone who is badly hurt."

She lived her life in this manner, reaching out to the poorest of the poor, the neediest of the needy. And in this, she taught us all life's biggest lesson: It is in giving that we receive.

What we receive is not just material things or even the satisfaction of a job well done. We are rewarded with joy, pure undiluted joy that can only arise when we extend a helping hand to another.

The next time you find yourself frustrated at the lack of love in your own life or at the lack of love in the world, try an experiment. Forget about the world and other people for a few minutes. Instead, look into your own heart. Can you become a source of greater love? Can you think loving thoughts for yourself and others? Can you extend these loving thoughts outwards towards the rest of the world, even to people whom you feel do not deserve it?

By opening your heart to the possibility of greater love and by making yourself a source of love (rather than getting love) as a top priority, you will be taking an important step in getting the love you desire.

You will also discover something truly remarkable. The more love you give, the more you will receive. As you put more emphasis on being a loving person, which is something you can control, and less emphasis on receiving love, which is something you cannot control, you will find that you have plenty of love in your life.

Soon you will discover one of the greatest secrets in the world: Love is its own reward.

Realise the Power of Your Own Thoughts

If you were to become aware of only one mental dynamic, the most important one to know about would be the relationship between your thinking and the way you feel.

It is important to realise that you are constantly thinking. Think, for a moment, about your breathing. Until this moment, when you are reading this sentence, you had certainly lost sight of the fact that you were doing it. The truth is, unless you are out of breath, you simply forget that it is occurring.

> If you live your life thinking that you will be happy 'tomorrow', let me tell you straight off that tomorrow never comes

Thinking works in the same way. Because you are always doing it, it is easy to forget that it is happening, and it becomes invisible to you. Unlike breathing, however, forgetting that you are thinking can cause some serious problems in your life, such as unhappiness, anger, inner conflicts and stress.

The reason this is true is that your thinking will always come back to you as a feeling; there is a point-to-point relationship.

Try getting angry without first having angry thoughts! Then try feeling stressed out without first having stressful thoughts, or sad without sad thoughts, or jealous without thoughts of jealousy. You cannot do it, it is impossible. For, in order to experience a feeling, you must first have a thought that produces that feeling.

Realise that unhappiness does not and cannot exist on its own. Unhappiness is the feeling that accompanies negative thinking about your life.

In the complete absence of that thinking, unhappiness, or stress, or jealousy, cannot exist. There is nothing to hold your negative feelings in place other than your own thinking. Remind yourself that it is your thinking that is negative, not your life. This simple awareness will be the first step in putting you back on the path towards happiness.

Bless Today: It will Never Come Again

It is fine to work towards future goals, but do not forget that today will never come again. You have only twenty-four hours to enjoy it. If you live your life thinking that you will be happy 'tomorrow', let me tell you straight off that tomorrow never comes. It just becomes your present, your today.

And you go on planning and fretting and worrying about something that actually does not exist.

Some people put life on hold while striving for their dreams. At first their objective is, "After I attain 'whatever', then I'll be happy." Then, later, after the success of attainment, they are regretful. "Why didn't I take time to plant a garden?" (or to play with my children, to visit old friends, be kinder to my partner, relax, or go to the movies, or go hiking?).

Instead of waiting to be an old lady to wear purple, wear it now. Instead of waiting for retirement to live in a beautiful place, consider how to get there now.

So if you feel your life is filled with remorse and dissatisfaction, stop and ask yourself these five questions:

1. What is missing in my life?
2. What have I put on hold?
3. What am I waiting for?
4. What would really fill my heart and make me happy?
5. What would I regret if I died tomorrow?

Pause at the last question. Though you may not die tomorrow, the saddest death is walking around like a robot, cut off from the magic of today, from love, from beauty, from being where you want to be.

A wonderful way to begin the day is to bless it. You could perhaps start your day by keeping a single minute aside for saying the following:

Blessings on this day, may I make it special in some way.
Blessings on my life, may I treat it with love and care.
Blessings on all people, may I see the goodness in everyone.
Blessings on nature, may I notice its beauty and wonder.
Blessings on the truth, may it be my constant companion.

Learn to Live in the Present Moment

To a large degree, the measure of our peace of mind is determined by how much we are able to live in the present moment. Without question, many of us spend much of our lives worrying about a variety of things, all at once. We allow past problems and future

★ Many people live as if life were a dress rehearsal for some later date. It is not. In fact, no one has a guarantee that he or she will be here tomorrow ★

concerns to dominate our present moments, so much so that we end up anxious, frustrated, depressed and hopeless. On the flip side, we also postpone our gratifications, our stated priorities and our happiness, often convincing ourselves that 'some day' will be better than today.

Unfortunately, the same mental dynamics that tell us to look towards the future will only repeat themselves so that 'some day' never actually arrives.

John Lennon once said that life is what happens while we're busy making other plans.

When we are busy making 'other plans', our children are busy growing up, the people we love are moving away and dying, our bodies are getting out of shape, and our dreams are slipping away.

In short, we miss out on life.

Many people live as if life were a dress rehearsal for some later date. It is not.

In fact, no one has a guarantee that he or she will be here tomorrow. When our attention is in the present moment, we push fear from our minds. Fear is the concern over events that might happen in the future—we will not have enough money, our children will get into trouble, we will get old and die, and so on. To combat fear, the best strategy is to learn to bring your attention back to the present.

Mark Twain said, "I have been through some terrible things in my life, some of which actually happened."

> ★ Instead of waiting for retirement to live in a beautiful place, consider how to get there now ★

I don't think I can say it any better. Practise keeping your attention on the here and now. Your efforts will pay great dividends.

Step 4

Live in the present

This moment is your only reality

| Chapter Five |

Your Thoughts Make Your Reality

If you want to be unhappy, no one in the world can make you happy. And if you determine to be happy, no one in the world will be able to make you unhappy.

Paramahansa Yogananda

A simple thought. A few micro-milliwatts of energy flowing through our brain; a seemingly innocuous, almost ephemeral thing. And yet a thought or, more accurately, a carefully orchestrated series of thoughts, has a significant impact on our mind, our body and our emotions.

Thoughts have responses in the body. Think of a lemon. Imagine cutting it in half and removing the seeds with the point of a knife. Smell the lemon. Now, imagine squeezing the juice from the lemon into your mouth and digging your teeth into the centre of the lemon. Chew the pulp.

Feel those little things (whatever those are called) breaking and popping inside your mouth. Most people's salivary glands respond to the very thought of a lemon.

For some people, the mere thought of the sound of fingernails on a chalkboard is physically uncomfortable. Try this: Imagine an emery board or a fingernail file or a double-sided piece of sandpaper. Imagine putting it in your mouth. Bite down on it. Now move your teeth from side to side. Goosebumps?

Thoughts influence our emotions. Think of something you love. What do you feel? Now think of something you hate. What do you feel? Now, something you love again. We do not have to change our emotions consciously, just change our thoughts, and our emotions quickly follow.

Thoughts have power over our mind, our body and our emotions

Now imagine your favourite place in nature. Where is it? A beach? A meadow? A mountain top? Imagine lying on your back, with your eyes closed. Feel the sun on your face. Smell the air. Hear the sounds of creation. Become a part of it. Relax.

Most people who take the time to try these little experiments know what I am talking about. Those who thought, "This stuff is silly. I'm not going to try anything as stupid as this!" are left with the emotional and physiological consequences of their thoughts, perhaps a sense of tightness, irritability, impatience or maybe outright hostility. These people prove the point I am making, as do those who follow along with the 'suggested' thoughts. The point being: thoughts have power over our mind, our body and our emotions.

Positive thoughts (joy, happiness, fulfilment, achievement and worthiness) have positive results (enthusiasm, calm, well-being, ease, energy and love). Negative thoughts (judgement, unworthiness, mistrust, resentment and fear) produce negative results (tension, anxiety, alienation, anger and fatigue).

Understanding as to why something as miniscule as a thought can have such a dramatic effect on our mind, body and emotions helps us to interpret the automatic reaction human beings have whenever they perceive danger—the fight or flight response.

Negative Thoughts and the Body

The fight or flight response puts a body through its paces. All the resources of the body are mobilised for immediate physical action, to fight or flee. All the other bodily functions are put on hold.

In addition to this, the body is pumping chemicals, naturally produced drugs, into the system. The muscles need energy and they need it fast. Our body has armed itself to fight or flee for its life, and usually we just sit and seethe.

The repeated and unnecessary triggering of the fight or flight response puts enormous physiological stress on the body. It makes us vulnerable to diseases such as digestive troubles (ulcers and cancers at the far side of it), poor assimilation (preventing necessary proteins, vitamins and minerals from entering the system), slower recovery from illnesses (conquering a disease is far less important than conquering a wild beast), reduced production of blood cells and other necessary cells, sore muscles and a general sense of fatigue. The emergency chemicals, unused, eventually begin breaking down into other, more toxic substances. Our body must then mobilise yet again, to get rid of these poisons.

The muscles stay tense for a long time after the response is triggered, this is especially so around the stomach, chest, lower back, neck and shoulders. (Most people have chronic tension in at least one of these areas.) We feel jittery, nervous and uptight.

★ Because people are afraid of fear, they give up acre after acre of their own lives. Some find the snapping of twigs so uncomfortable that they abandon the territory of life altogether ★

The mind always tries to find reasons for things. If the body is feeling uptight, it wonders, "What is there to feel uptight about?" Seldom do we conclude (correctly), "Oh, this is just the normal after-effects of the fight or flight response. Nothing to be concerned about."

Usually we start scanning the environment (inner and outer) for something out of place. And, as mentioned before, there will always be something out of place.

The mind is a remarkable mechanism. Given a task, it will fulfil it with astounding speed and accuracy. When asked, "What's wrong?" it will compile and cross-reference a list of grievances with blinding swiftness and precision. Everything everyone (including ourselves) should have done but did not do is reviewed, highlighted, indexed and prioritised. All this is sparked by a sensation in the body. Naturally, this mental review of negative events prompts a new round of fight or flight responses, which promotes more tension in the body, and more mental investigation into what is wrong.

Do you see how this downward mind/body spiral can continue almost indefinitely?

When this spiral continues for a while, it is generally known as depression. But because depression, we hear, is a form of mental illness, which is considered bad by our culture and society, we feel depressed about feeling that way, and a whole new cycle of the fight or flight response is then triggered in an almost alarming proportion.

Considering all this, it is not surprising that some people make a decision deep inside themselves that life is just not worth living. They enter a deep, dark world whose innermost recesses are lined with negative thoughts. Captured in this world of their making, they remain forever unhappy.

Negative Thoughts and Emotions

The primary emotions generated by the fight or flight response are anger (the emotional energy to fight) and fear (the emotional energy to flee).

Contained within these two are most of the feelings we generally associate with the word 'negative'.

Consider these lists:

ANGER	FEAR
hostility	terror
resentment	anxiety
guilt (anger at oneself)	timidity
rage	shyness (a general fear of others)
seething	withdrawal
depression	reticence
hurt (you are usually upset with someone else, or grieving yourself, or both)	apprehension (fear that you will never love or be loved again)

Any others you did care to add from your own repertoire could probably be considered a variation of anger or fear—or a combination of the two.

The problem with either emotion, in addition to the obvious unpleasantness, is that both tend to lead us close to logical, rational, life-supporting decisions.

How often have you waded into a confrontation, only to find that you had, in all probability, as the saying goes, stirred up a hornet's nest?

How many fields have you abandoned in your life? The field of a challenging new career? The field of a more fulfilling place to live? The field of relationships? (That's 'relationships' as in 'true love, a many-splendoured thing'.) The field of your dreams?

Because people are afraid of fear, they give up acre after acre of their own lives. Some find the snapping of twigs so uncomfortable that they tend to abandon the territory of life altogether.

The Addictive Quality of Negative Thinking

For many, negative thinking becomes a bad habit that, over time, degenerates into an addiction. It is a disease, such as alcoholism, compulsive over-eating or drug abuse. A lot of people suffer from this disease because negative thinking is addictive to each of these three—the mind, the body and the emotions.

The mind becomes addicted to being 'right'. In this far-less-than-perfect world, one of the easiest ways to be right is to predict failure, especially for ourselves. The mind likes being right. When asked "Would you rather be right or be happy?", some people, who really take the time to consider the ramifications of being 'wrong', have trouble deciding.

The body becomes addicted to the rush of chemicals poured into the blood stream by the fight or flight response. The thrill of a serious session of negative thinking is something of a high. Some people 'get off' on the rush of adrenaline.

The emotions become addicted to the sheer intensity of it all. They may not be pleasant feelings, but they are a long way from boredom. As the emotions become acclimated to a certain level of stimulation, they start demanding more and more intensity.

Let's take a pause here. I can almost imagine that some of my readers are wondering why I am dwelling for so long on the topic of negativity and all that goes with it. How does all this fit in a manual of happiness? Well, the answer, the way I see it, is pretty obvious. Negative thoughts are deadly, dangerous and depressing. Positive thoughts are the exact opposite of that—they are life enhancing and joyful. Knowing one gives insights into the other.

Negative thoughts are deadly, dangerous and depressing. Positive thoughts are the exact opposite of that—they are life enhancing and joyful

To my mind, negative thinking must be treated like any addiction, with commitment to life, patience, discipline, a will to get better, forgiveness, self-love and the knowledge that recovery is not just possible without following certain guidelines. Here are twenty simple, commonsense strategies that you can use for transforming mental, physical and emotional tension into energy that is creative and effective. This energy gets rid of stress and ensures that you are happy at all times.

I would suggest that you follow these steps consciously. Make every effort to incorporate them into your life. Soon you will find that you are practising them without even being aware of any attempt on your part. And then twenty will not seem such a formidable figure, but something that is very doable.

Step 1: *Be by yourself*

Take time to be alone on a regular basis, to listen to your heart, check your intentions, re-evaluate your goals and your activities. Solitude is precious; a person who loves his or her company is forever happy. He or she does not need to rely on another for joy. Being alone gives you the time to reflect and decide on your priorities.

Identify a place where you will not be disturbed—a rocking chair in the corner of your sitting room, say. Make yourself comfortable; close your eyes and listen to your inner voice. It will never let you down.

Step 2: *Simplify your life*

Start eliminating the trivial things. Also, don't major in minor things. This is time for you to get rid of all the extra baggage in your life. Watch the mental kilograms disappearing; see yourself lighten.

Step 3: *Breathe in and out slowly*

Take deep, slow breaths frequently, especially while on the telephone, in the car, or waiting for something or someone.

Use any opportunity to relax and revitalise yourself. Carefully watch the space between the external and internal breaths; many of you could even experience the joys associated with meditation here.

Step 4: *Be nice to yourself*

Plan to do something each day that brings you joy, something that you love to do, something just for *you*. This activity could involve re-reading a favourite book; enjoying a bar of chocolate or meeting a special friend. The happiness generated by any of these activities will linger on; bringing happiness whenever you re-live the moment.

★ Solitude is precious; a person who loves his or her company is forever happy. He or she does not need to rely on another for joy ★

Step 5: *Express yourself*

When you're concerned about something, talk it over with someone you trust, or write down your feelings. Both these acts work as therapies—often, just by sharing your problems and worries with someone or even with a diary, you find that the problem does not exist. It vanishes simply because you have unburdened yourself and got it out of your system. The end result? A visibly lighter and happier you.

Step 6: *Learn to say 'No'*

Say 'No' in a firm but kind way when asked to do something

you really don't want to do. This is much better than doing something unwillingly and unhappily. The task will seem like a burden and you will not enjoy a moment of it. Or, on the other hand, by refusing in the nicest, politest manner, may bring relief to all.

Step 7: *Exercise regularly*

Stretching your body releases tension. Any form of physical activity—aerobics, walking, dancing, yoga—not only nurtures your body, it is good for your mind as well. The hormones released will make you happy. So find time for your favourite kind of exercise, even if it is for just fifteen minutes a day. It will make a difference.

Step 8: *Do it now*

Remember, it takes less energy to get an unpleasant task done 'right now' than to worry about it all day. The thought of it will be there, right with you, throughout the day. You will not be able to enjoy whatever you are doing or give it your best attention if, at the back of your mind, you know that you have some unfinished business.

Step 9: *Be with nature*

Take time to be with nature. Even in the city, noticing the seasonal changes of the sky can be a good harmoniser. Try to go for a walk in the park and observe all the trees and the birds. This is a great mood elevator. I really know of no one who comes back unhappy after communing with nature.

Step 10: *Be aware of what you are doing*

I am not a great one for multitasking. On the contrary, I think it is important to live in the moment, love what you are doing and give it your hundred per cent. Practise consciously doing one thing at a time, keeping your mind focussed on the present. Do whatever you're doing more slowly, more intentionally, and with more awareness and respect.

★ It takes less energy to get an unpleasant task done 'right now' than to worry about it all day ★

Step 11: *Stop worrying*

Choose not to waste your precious present life on guilt about the past or concern for the future. Worry and the accompanying stress cause misery. Can you visualise someone who is constantly thinking about the future or carrying some guilt-ridden thoughts as being happy?

Step 12: *Meditate*

There's lot more on meditation and its unbelievable, magical properties in *The Little Manual of Meditation*, but I think it will not be amiss to dwell on this topic if one is truly looking for happiness. Learn a variety of relaxation techniques and practise meditation regularly.

Many of us are sceptical at first. We tend to look at meditation as something that the holy men in the Himalayas do. Or, we say, it works for others, but I simply do not have the time. Take my word for it—make the time for meditation, *now*.

Meditation has benefits on many different levels. It works on the physical body and through it goes deeper to the emotional and mental self of the practitioner. Those who sustain the practice find many spiritual benefits as well. It's easy to learn and can be practised almost anywhere, including in your office or car while commuting.

There are literally hundreds of meditation techniques and you can always find one suitable to you and the environment at hand. Its overall long-lasting effect on your mental frame of mind cannot be over-emphasised.

Step 13: *Control your temper*

Remember, the person who loses his/her temper, loses. There's no getting out of this one. An angry person is just not likeable. And, it follows, an angry person is not happy. When you find yourself angry in situations, ask yourself, "What can I learn from this?" Anyone or anything that can make you angry is showing you how you let yourself be controlled by expectations of how someone or something should be.

When we accept others, ourselves and situations for what they are, we become more effective in influencing them to change in the way that we'd like them to. We react to them in a more positive manner. Instead of losing our cool, we remain calm.

Step 14: *Do not be demanding*

Become more aware of the demands you place on yourself,

your environment and on others to be different from how they are at any moment. Demands are tremendous sources of stress and unhappiness.

Step 15: *Prioritise*

If your schedule is busy, prioritise your activities and do the most important ones first. It is really as simple as that. Get the more important stuff out of the way. Keep your 'out' basket of life in order; with the more essential tasks right on the top. This works both at the office and at home.

Step 16: *Take it easy*

We all tend to make our lives like roller coasters. We are rushing from one place to another, running after all kinds of crazy deadlines. These play havoc with your peace of mind. So organise your life to include time for fun, spontaneity and open spaces. Set a realistic schedule, allowing some transition time between your activities. Also, try to eliminate all the unnecessary commitments.

Step 17: *Laugh*

> Organise your life to include time for fun, spontaneity and open spaces

Smile and laugh more. Be kinder to yourself and others. You do not have to be judgemental and harsh. Learn to relax. Laughing is a great stress-buster, haven't you heard of all those laughing clubs that are mushrooming everywhere? People just get together to raise their hands and have a jolly good laugh.

They feel so happy doing this that the practice becomes addictive. The Indian spiritual Master, Osho, referred to laughter as the essential religion. I agree. Laughter is a manifestation of your frame of mind. A happy person will obviously be ready to laugh. You do not need to wait for World Happiness Day, the first Sunday in the month of May, to raise your hands and have a good, hearty laugh. Do it on any day, especially when you are feeling low. This activity itself, the act of conscious, even enforced, laughter is contagious.

Step 18: *Delegate*

You cannot do everything. Accept that. However good you are—as a parent, office worker, whatever—you need to let go. You need to allow others to help you meet goals. Learn to delegate responsibility. You may be in for a surprise.

People are capable of good work if you trust them and make them responsible for certain tasks. Have you not noticed how happy a little girl looks if she is told that she is baking that yummy chocolate cake, and not her mom?

Step 19: *Eat right*

Monitor your intake of sugar, salt, caffeine and alcohol. Add the veggies and all that green stuff in your diet.

Step 20: *Welcome change*

View change as an opportunity and challenge to learn and grow. If life was to go on in the same way, the same routine day after day, there may be no disasters, but then there will be no learning opportunities as well. Do not let a change upset you and make you unhappy.

If you have read all these twenty steps, and absorbed their simple lessons, you will realise that being happy encompasses so much; yet it takes so little to be happy. Do not look at externals for sources of happiness; look inside. A walk, time spent with a loved one, a good book—they all make for a happy you, a person with happy thoughts.

★ Laughter is a manifestation of your frame of mind. A happy person will obviously be ready to laugh ★

Step 5

Think happy thoughts

Negativity never enters a trained mind

| Chapter Six |

Create Constant Happiness

Happiness is a continuous creative activity.

Baba Amte

Creativity is powerful. It is a gift. It teaches us to connect with our special talents. Happiness allows us to create positive thoughts that lead us to a path of fulfilment.

Thoughts are also powerful. All the spectacular and terrible creations of humanity began as thoughts—an idea, if you will. From the idea came the plan and from the plan came the action and from the action came the object. Whatever you are sitting on or reclining upon began as a thought. The room you are in, and almost everything in it, began as a thought.

All the wars and fighting the world has known began with thoughts. All the good, fine, noble and creative acts of humanity were conceived as a spark in a single human consciousness. The Eiffel Tower, the Mona Lisa, the Taj Mahal, the Declaration of Independence, movies, books, television, began in the human mind.

Even the creation of a human being began as a thought. As the old saying goes, "I knew you before you were a twinkle in your father's eye."

Victor Hugo described it this way: "An invasion of armies can be resisted, but not an idea whose time has come." Often misquoted as, "There is nothing so powerful as an idea whose time has come", it has been used so much that it has almost become a cliché.

★ Happiness allows us to create positive thoughts that lead us to a path of fulfilment ★

Although we probably do not think about it often, it is easy to see that everything created by humans, both the good and the bad, began as a thought. (The categorisation of 'good' and 'bad', of course, is just another thought.) The only difference between a thought and a physical reality is a certain amount of time and physical activity. The amount of time and physical activity varies from project to project. Sometimes it is seconds, sometimes it is years, and sometimes the thought must be passed from generation to generation.

Some of the great cathedrals took a century and three generations of stonecutters to complete. There has been a Hundred Years' War. Leonardo da Vinci invented the helicopter four hundred years before one ever flew. Two hundred years ago, Thomas Jefferson envisioned a nation free from religious persecution.

Some people are particularly good at turning ideas into realities. Edison was one. Imagine: the phonograph, movies, an improved telephone and the electric light all from one man. Henry Ford wanted to make a cheap, reliable automobile and invented the assembly line in order to do it.

Without thoughts, things that involve any sort of human action just do not happen.

Where we are is the result of a lifetime of thinking, both positive and negative. If you wonder what your thinking has been like, take a look at where you are in life. Behold the answer! Reflect on it.

If you are pleased with some parts of your life, then your thinking in those areas has no doubt been what you would generally call 'positive'.

If you are not pleased with other parts of your life, then your thoughts about those areas probably have not been as positive as they could have been. The good news is that thoughts can be easily changed, and with that change invariably come changes in manifestation.

Remember, what you think, you become. If you think and imagine yourself to be happy, you are happy.

Thoughts, if persisted in, can produce states of consciousness that, if persisted in, can produce physical manifestation. If you persist in your thoughts of wealth, for example, this produces a consciousness of wealth, an overall state of being that is open, accepting, abundant and flowing, and this consciousness of wealth tends to produce the physical manifestations of wealth—houses, cars, cash.

★ Where we put our vision, our inner and outer vision, is the direction we tend to go ★

"But," someone once protested, "I don't have any money and I worry about it all the time." This person was proving the point, but in reverse.

Worry is a form of fear, in this case a fear of poverty. This person, in holding an ongoing series of thoughts about poverty, created a consciousness of poverty, which created a lack of everything but bills, which caused more worry, and more poverty.

Positive thoughts yield positive results—loving, caring and sharing; health, wealth and happiness; prosperity, abundance and riches.

Negative thoughts invariably bring negative results—dislike, indifference and withholding; disease, poverty and misery; fear, lack and alienation.

Our thoughts create our physical reality. Where we put our vision, both inner and outer, is the direction we tend to go. The way we get there—well, there are many methods.

Why Do We Indulge in Negative Thinking?

Why do we use the power of our mind to create a negative reality? If our mind can generate health, wealth and happiness as easily as illness, poverty and despair, why are we not healthy, wealthy and happy all the time?

If a genie appeared and offered you a choice—health, wealth and happiness or illness, poverty and despair—which would you choose?

If positivity is the obvious choice, why do we sometimes choose the negative? There must be something else, something deeper within us generating the impulse to think negatively, even when we do not want to.

Although you may have another word—or words—to describe this phenomenon, I call this wellspring of negative thinking unworthiness. It is more than just a feeling or a passing thought. It is a ground of being, a deep-seated belief that "I'm just not good enough." Other phrases for it include insecurity, undeservingness or low self-esteem.

Unworthiness undermines all our positive ideas and validates all our negative thoughts.

When we think something good about ourselves, unworthiness pops up and says, "No, you're not." When we desire something positive for ourselves, unworthiness says, "You don't deserve it." When something good happens to us, unworthiness says, often with our own lips, "This is too good to be true!" When something bad happens to us, unworthiness is the first to point out, "See I was right all along. I told you so."

Some people cover their unworthiness with an air of self-confidence and an outward bravado bordering on arrogance. Their cover-up includes a self-indulgence and self-absorption that are almost selfish. These people, it appears on the surface, could use a healthy dose of unworthiness.

But, in reality, they are merely involved in a desperate attempt to hide, from themselves as much as from anyone else, the fact that they just do not feel worthy. They think the unworthiness is true, not just another illusion, and they respond by concealing it rather than laughing at it.

So where does unworthiness come from? A look at how children are raised might offer a clue.

Imagine a child, at two, three or four, playing alone in a room. An adult, usually a parent, is nearby. What for? To come in and praise the child every five minutes? No. The adult is there for "supervision" and to be on hand "in case there's any trouble". Actually, the adult is sitting there, anticipating trouble.

Unworthiness undermines all our positive ideas and validates all our negative thoughts

The child is playing and having a wonderful time. Two hours go by. The child is 'behaving' wonderfully. The interaction with the adult has been minimal.

Suddenly, the child knocks a lamp off the table. It crashes to the floor. What happens next?

Lots of interaction with the adult, almost all of which is negative. Yelling, screaming ("This was my favourite lamp," "How many times have I told you?" "Bad, bad, bad"), and probably, for good measure, some form of physical punishment (spanking, deprivation of a toy). Almost the only interaction in two hours from the adult community was, "You are bad. Shame on you."

As an infant, we get unconditional, almost never-ending praise. Once we grow a little older and begin exploring our world, our primary form of interaction with adults—the symbols of power, love, authority and life itself—is usually corrective. Suddenly we find the baby has entered the 'terrible twos' where everything comes with a lesson, however sugar-coated it may be.

If we draw a picture, we are praised for the first endeavour. The picture will be shown to doting aunts and uncles and there will be general excitement all around. But if the same picture is drawn again and again we are not praised and are asked to do something new.

Some children learn to do negative things just to get attention, because even negative attention is better than no attention at all. Being ignored, to a child, can seem like abandonment.

Without thoughts, things that involve any sort of human action just do not happen. Where we are is the result of a lifetime of thinking, both positive and negative

A part of us inside begins to add up all the times we are called "wonderful" and all the times we are called "bad".

The bad seems to outnumber the wonderful by a significant margin. We may begin to believe we are bad, that unless we do something new and remarkable, we are not going to be thought of as good; that we must strive, work hard and never disobey if we hope to get even a little appreciation in this world; that our goodness must be earned because we are, after all, essentially bad.

We may grow to believe this about ourselves, and from this fertile ground springs our negative thoughts. This could be the starting point for many insecurities. This is where many complexes are born. And these complexes ensure that we are not happy. They actually are the source of many depressions. They point the way to unhappiness because they make us feel unworthy and unloved. An unhappy person invariably harbours unworthy and negative thoughts and goes on to spread these to all he or she meets.

That is probably the reason why most of us tend to run away from these kind of people. They seem to be shrouded in an aura of negativity. Being with them is depressing. Even the happiest among us get a jolt in their company. Our positive thoughts of well-being are replaced with darker thoughts.

Simply put, a negative person radiates the kind of energy that we all want to avoid. He or she is convinced that, for them, life holds no meaning. They have only 'bad' and 'more bad' things to look forward to.

Then there are the 'mixed' people, a category in which most of us fall. These are the folks that have positive and negative thoughts and there is generally an interplay between them, depending on the present set of circumstances.

But often, even when we have a lot of positive thoughts, the negative ones tend to be more believed. A positive thought, checked against this belief of unworthiness, is labelled 'false'.

A negative thought feels right at home. The unworthiness proclaims it true, and right.

Negative thoughts often take over our entire perspective.

A person thinks negative, s/he talks negative and, it obviously follows, approaches all aspects of life with a predominant negative air.

Compare this to the Zen Master in this story: When he passed away, a blind man who lived nearby told a friend that as he was blind, he could not see a person, so all he could do to gauge a person's character was to listen to him: "Ordinarily when I hear someone congratulate another upon his happiness or success, I also hear a secret tone of envy. When condolence is expressed for the misfortune of another, I hear pleasure and satisfaction, as if the one condoling was really glad there was something left to gain in his own world. In all my experience, however, the Master's voice was always sincere. Whenever he expressed happiness, I heard nothing but happiness, and whenever he expressed sorrow, sorrow was all I heard."

★ Negative thoughts often take over our entire perspective. A person thinks negative, s/he talks negative and, it follows, approaches all aspects of life with a predominant negative air ★

Be like the Zen Master who knows no envy and holds no negative thought and see your life take a happy turn.

Step 6

Be positive always, all-ways

Happiness is created within you, in your mind

| Chapter Seven |

See the Sunshine, Not the Shadows

A happy life must be to a great extent a quiet life, for it is only in an atmosphere of quiet that true joy can live.

Bertrand Russell

In any given moment, there is ample evidence to prove that life is a bed of thorns or a garden of roses. How we feel about life depends on where we place our attention—that is, what we focus upon.

Did you ever notice that every time you are given a rose, the stem is covered with thorns? (If you take the thorns off, the flower wilts more quickly. Florists know this and, therefore, leave the thorns on.) Do you say, "Why are you giving me this stick with thorns on it?" Of course not. You admire the beauty of the rose. Even if you prick yourself in your enthusiasm, it never seems to hurt—you are too involved in appreciating the rose and the person who gave it to you.

Right now, without moving from where you are, you can find ample evidence to prove that your life is a miserable, depressing, terrible burden, or you can find evidence to prove your life is an abundant, joyful, exciting adventure.

You can either choose to connect with joy or you may opt for a disconnect with all that brings joy.

Let us start with the negative. Look at all the imperfections around you. No matter how good anything is, it could be better, could it not? Look for dirt, disorder and dust. See all the things that need cleaning, repairing and replacing. An endless array of clutter, chaos and catastrophe assaults your senses. Now, let go of the complaining consciousness and look at the situation with an attitude of gratitude and appreciation.

Look around the same area you just surveyed and find the good. You can start with whatever you are sitting or lying on. It is probably softer than a concrete floor. Look at all the other objects you use but take for granted such as glasses (both seeing and drinking), tables, windows, the walls and the ceiling sheltering you from the elements. Consider the wonder of the electric light. A hundred years ago, you would have to have been very rich or very lucky to have had even one. And today you probably have a dozen and a television set or two and a radio and many of the other electronic marvels of the age.

How we feel about life depends on where we place our attention—that is, what we focus upon

What around you do you find aesthetically pleasing?

A painting you have not really looked at in years? The pattern on the clothes you are wearing? A flower? A vase? Wallpaper? Carpet? When was the last time you took a moment to appreciate colours?

Did you notice that you have tended to feel better when you focussed on the positive things in your surroundings? The process of focussing on the positive to produce more positive feelings works the same with things more intimate than your surroundings—your body, for example.

If you look for all the things wrong with the body, pains here, bumps there, rough spots over here, too much fat; the list goes on then. But take a look at all that is right with your body. Even if you have a pain in your left foot, you can be thankful there is not one in your right.

You do not have to adopt what is best referred to as an ostrich attitude. On the contrary, be aware of what you have and what you do not have. Accept what you have graciously. Look for people who you could share all your goodies with, people who would truly enjoy them. Focus on the bright spots but also look at what is missing.

To focus on the positive is not to disregard certain warning signals of a 'negative' nature that, if ignored, eventually lead to inconvenience at best and disaster at worst. (If we use these 'negative' signals to avoid disaster, then they are not so negative after all. Some even call them guardian angels.)

Let us say you are driving down the road and the little light goes on, indicating that you are running out of fuel. I do not suggest ignoring that bit of 'negativity' and focussing on how wonderful it is that none of the other warning lights are on. I suggest you get some fuel quickly.

To focus on the positive is not to disregard certain warning signals of a 'negative' nature that, if ignored, eventually lead to inconvenience at best and disaster at worst

Here, by the way, is where the negative thinking can come in. The negative reality is that you are low on gas. Negative thinking begins the litany, "I wonder if I'm going to run out of gas before I arrive at the next station. What will I do if that happens?" During this inner tirade the driver, in his or her anxiety, usually speeds up, which only wastes gas.

What I suggest is this—take note of the negative information, decide what to do about it (whatever corrective action seems to be in order) and, while doing it, return to focussing upon the positive while working on 'eliminating' the negative.

With medical conditions, it is good to keep track of symptoms, but it does no good to dwell upon them. The positive thinker might deny the early symptoms of a disease, making a cure all the more difficult. The negative thinkers might turn every mosquito bite into skin cancer.

Those with a positive approach take a middle road. They note symptoms accurately so that they can be reported to their healthcare provider. They make an appointment. Beyond that, there is no point in dwelling on the symptoms, so they turn their attention to things more positive. And thus remain happy.

Have I made a clear distinction between positive thinking and focussing on the positive? It is a subtle but important difference. Positive thinking imagines any wonderful thing, no matter how unrelated it may be to the actual events of one's life.

Focussing on the positive starts with what is so, what is real, what is actually taking place, and moves forward from there in a joyful direction.

If you spend all your time in a positive future, when will you appreciate the present? The present is the future you dreamed of long ago. Enjoy it!

Figure Out what You Do Not Want in Your Life

In addition to figuring out what your priorities are, it is also helpful to figure out what you do not want in your life any more. This is a subtle distinction, but it is an important one to make.

We allow a lot of mental, emotional and psychological clutter to accumulate in our minds and our lives, blocking our access to inner peace. This is the kind of garbage that we must dispose of, almost immediately.

This clutter includes doing things we do not want to do but continue to do, either because we used to do them or feel we should. It includes spending time with people we no longer want to spend time with because we have simply outgrown the relationship or because they do not contribute to our inner growth.

It includes doing work we are not happy doing.

It includes trying to do too many things, even if a lot of them are things we do not want to do.

It includes not doing enough of the things we want to do.

It includes engaging in idle gossip and meaningless chatter that drains our energy.

An amazing amount of the clutter includes fuming over past events we cannot change, or being distracted by future events that may never happen. It includes judgement and harbouring thoughts that burn.

★ Positive thinking imagines any wonderful thing, no matter how unrelated it is to the actual events of one's life ★

As you move towards developing harmony in your life, you will find that a lot of this stuff will fall by the wayside. Some things, however, will require an effort on your part to make sure they are eliminated.

Enjoy Each Moment

One of the ultimate objectives of attaining inner simplicity is learning to live happily in the present moment.

Keep in mind that life is a continuous succession of present moments. Most of us spend an inordinate number of our moments regretting the past, or fidgeting in the present, or worrying about the future.

Worry and regret and being anxious are habits that keep us locked in old patterns. But these habits can be eliminated once we have become aware of them.

If you find such habits are getting in the way of being happy, think about what you can do to change them. It sounds simplistic to say it, but you can get into the habit of enjoying your life.

Another way to choose to enjoy each moment is to start taking responsibility for your life. If you are not happy in your present circumstances, you have no one but yourself to blame. Make whatever changes you need to make sure that you are happy. Keep saying to yourself that you alone are responsible for the circumstances. They are of your making. Go within and try to find answers. This will automatically bring you to a level of enjoyment of your day-to-day life that you may not have experienced before. Making the conscious effort to enjoy each moment will make your inner quest much easier.

Connect with the Sun

All the enlightened cultures of the past, and many sages of the present, recognise the role the sun plays in getting us in touch with our soul. We know our bodies need the sun in order to maximise the vitamins and minerals we get from our food. Yet, we now spend close to ninety per cent of our time in artificial light.

★ If you are not happy in your present circumstances, you have no one but yourself to blame. Make whatever changes you need to make sure that you are happy ★

Numerous studies have shown the debilitating effects on many people of the absence of adequate sunlight. Medical science has also recently acknowledged the existence of SAD (seasonal affective disorder) and the need for sunlight for certain personality types.

One of the simplest ways to brighten up your mood is to step into the sunlight. Brief, definitely not extensive, exposure to the sun's rays is tremendously beneficial to our overall physical, mental and emotional health. But, most important, linking with the sun increases our vitality and also elevates our consciousness, thereby contributing to our inner growth and mental make-up.

Whenever you can, get ten to fifteen minutes of full exposure to the sun, either early in the morning or later in the day. In winter, sit next to a sunny window to get a mini sunbath.

Experiment with this. Connect with the sun every day for the next couple of weeks to see how beneficial it can be towards expanding your inner awareness.

Do a Good Deed

This may sound strange to some of you, though I am quite sure that the majority will agree with me; helping someone is actually helping yourself. I find that the moment I do something 'good', it could even be something as basic as helping a visually challenged person cross the road, I feel good. I feel as if I have done something worthwhile. Visit a hospital, read to the sick and infirm, reach out to the needy—and you experience the most wonderful sense of fulfilment.

It could be the silent blessings and the abundant good wishes of the person/s you may have helped. But the feeling of good stays, like a wonderful fragrance, lighting up your day. A recent study carried out in Kentucky, USA, shows that being good to others brings meaning to your life, giving you a sense of well-being and happiness.

Rethink the Beliefs of Your Childhood

The number of people who have abandoned the religion of their childhood is legion. Many people are able to leave and never look back. Others leave, but are often consumed with guilt for doing so. Some people spend years feeling angry and bitter about the restrictive, small-minded thinking they have spent their lives overcoming. And many continue to feel adversely affected, sometimes unconsciously, by the dogma and the belief systems that permeated their minds as children.

> I find that the moment I do something 'good', it could even be something as basic as helping a visually challenged person cross the road, I feel good

There are also those who never had a childhood religion to leave behind, and who still basically believe in nothing. And there are many others who have allowed the predominant conclusion of pseudo-science, which says if we cannot prove it, it does not exist, to rule their thinking.

If you are beginning to take a look at your life, this may be a good time to examine any feelings you may have about the teaching of your childhood that could be holding you back from questions you really want to explore.

As you start to slow down and enjoy the silence and the solitude, as you learn to listen and begin to trust your intuition, as you start to make the changes in your lifestyle and habit patterns that will enable you to connect with your own truth, you will experience a new way of looking at life and the world and your place in it.

Rethink Your Current Beliefs

While you are rethinking the beliefs of your childhood, do not forget to examine your current beliefs, the ones you may have acquired after you let go of the beliefs of your childhood, the ones you moved into at the time of your mid-life crisis, or even the ones you settled into last year, or possibly last week. It will be helpful to stay open to new interpretations of the world and how it might work. Often we get stuck in our current thinking because, like an old shoe, it is so comfortable. Move out of your comfort zone from time to time, and keep an open mind.

Stop Worrying

Worry, like negative thinking, is a habit. And, like negative thinking or any other habit, it can be broken once we become aware of it. But worry is sometimes so subtle and so insidious and so pervasive in our society that we can worry for years and not even be aware of it.

I learned this lesson a few years ago when I had completed a major project. After months of long, hard work and many sleepless nights (when I would lie awake worrying if everything would be all right), finally the deadline was met and the project was completed. There was not a single thing more I could possibly do to make it better.

But one night a few weeks later, before I had a chance to start another project, I realised I was still waking in the middle of the night and lying there worrying about my completed project, even though there was nothing at all to worry about. Perhaps this same thing has happened to you.

As I lay there in bed, I had one of those experiences we all have from time to time. I saw in a flash that I have been moving through life from one worry to the next. I examined each of the circumstances as I could remember them, and it become clear that not only had there never been anything to worry about, but worry had never served any useful function. It was a total waste of energy that kept me from experiencing the joy of the moment and from getting any real sense of accomplishment from my work.

Move out of your comfort zone from time to time, and keep an open mind

A worry-free life is incredibly liberating and it will help you achieve inner peace.

Take Responsibility for Your Life

I believe that, metaphysically, we choose all the circumstances of our lives—our parents, our health, our physical characteristics, our race and our cultural and geographical orientation—before we are born, and that we come into this life knowing, at some level, that we have to use those circumstances for our inner growth. I also know that if I see my life as my responsibility, then I can make the necessary changes to create what I want and need to be happy.

If I take the position that someone else, a supreme power or whoever, is in charge and will take care of everything, I could be stuck for ages in circumstances I am not happy about and feel powerless to change them. I have learned that if there is something in my life that does not work, and I am waiting for someone else to fix it, I had better not be holding my breath. Nowhere is this more applicable than in the inner realms. If you are already taking responsibility for the outer areas of your life, it will be easier to make the choices you need to make for your spiritual growth.

Accept the Things You Cannot Change

Taking responsibility for your life also means accepting the things you cannot change.

If you are short and want to be tall, or you are an endomorph and wish you were an ectomorph, if you were born with some impediment or acquired one along the way, or if you find yourself in any particular set of circumstances that are absolute, immutable and irreversible, then you basically have two options. You can rant and rave and curse and indulge in remorse or guilt or self-pity. Or you can go along and deal with the situation and play the game the best you can.

You can be open to the possibility that those who say we have chosen our circumstances are correct, and then set about figuring out what you can learn from your life by making the most of it. When you look at the personal limitations someone like Helen Keller had to deal with, and the extent to which she overcame them, not to mention the tremendous contribution she made with her life, you can see that it is possible to fight with the inescapable and win.

> ★ Taking responsibility for your life also means accepting the things you cannot change ★

Going within to find the meaning of our life does not mean seeking to avoid the challenges our circumstances present. Rather it means finding the grace to learn how to live our lives to the fullest extent possible—whatever that is for us—and in the acceptance to move on to the highest level of growth.

Get Comfortable with Change

Growth by definition requires change.

If you have spent years with certain habits, beliefs and ways of doing things, inner growth may cause some upheaval in your life. Do not be put off by that. Get comfortable with it. Welcome it. Change offers an exciting, often exhilarating, way of getting in touch with your soul.

But if you find yourself stuck in outdated habits and ways of operating that no longer serve you, spend some time thinking about how you might do things differently.

True inner growth might well require that you experience new thoughts, new feelings, new sensations and new friendships, possibly even a new identity. Allow yourself to be vulnerable and open yourself to change.

Get Out of Relationships that Do Not Support You

We humans, for the most part, still maintain our herd instincts. It is comforting to be one of the pack, and to have family, friends and loved ones nearby to help us grow, at least at the start of our journey.

But it sometimes happens that the people we are closest to do not really support us. Look around you, not just at your spouse and the family members you are involved with, but at all the relationships and associations you have in your life.

The lack of support can be so subtle. We can hang out for years with someone we love and think of as a friend before we begin to realise that the relationship is not really helping us and, in fact, has been holding us back.

It is easy to be deceived by the comfort a long-time relationship appears to offer you. There is a certain ease that comes with familiarity and from knowing each other's history, and from the history the two of you have built together, even when it has been tumultuous.

But there comes a time when you have to ask some hard questions: Do those persons really love you, or are they hanging on to you because of their own lack or their own needs? They may say they love you, but do they make you feel loved? Are they really with you in your successes, or do they always manage to put you in the wrong? Do they love you enough to let you go on to bigger and better things, even if it means that they get left behind?

Non-acceptance and subtle put-downs can be powerful deterrents to your growth. If you are not getting the love and support you need from the relationships in your life, it will be much harder for you to achieve inner happiness.

☆ True inner growth might well require that you experience new thoughts, new feelings, new sensations and new friendships, possibly even a new identity ☆

If you are moving on, sometimes there is really no choice but to leave behind those who may not be ready to move on with you. Often you simply have to retreat with a smile, and gradually but resolutely reduce their presence in your life.

Realise that all the family ties and friendships in our lives are there for a purpose, but they are not necessarily meant to last forever. It takes a certain grace to recognise when the time for a disabling relationship is over and, even if the other person does not recognise it, to bow out and move on. You will then have the time and energy to concentrate on loving, supportive relationships.

Explore Meditation

Let me begin this section with the story of an enlightened Master who was meeting people and answering their queries.

"Master, I am unhappy. Can you give me the secret of happiness?" asked one.

"Yes I can," said the Master, "but before I do, you must know yourself."

"I am a failure in my business, dear Master. Can you show me how to succeed in business and in life?"

"Yes I can. But you must know yourself first," replied the wise Master.

"I have no love in my life," lamented another. "Can you tell me how I can find a loving partner for life?"

"Of course I can," answered the enlightened one. "But before you understand how, you must know yourself."

"I am in search of God. Can you take me to Him?" queried a spiritual disciple.

"Yes I can," said the Master with a smile, "but before you see God, you must know yourself."

No matter what the question, the Master had only one answer: You must know yourself. Know thyself: in this one sentence lie the solutions to all our sufferings and the secrets to all our desires. The human mind is the creator of our happiness or unhappiness, joy or sorrow, pleasure or pain, freedom or bondage, stress or relaxation, good or bad, failure or success. And by understanding oneself, one understands the mind and how to create what is beneficial for us and others and desist from the unconscious creation of what pains us and others. Meditation is one of the most powerful tools we have for self-expansion and inner growth.

Through meditation we can reach levels of mental clarity that we cannot achieve through any other means. Meditation is a major pathway to the soul.

There are many ways to meditate. You can meditate on the inflow and outflow of the breath. You can meditate using a sacred word or phrase. You can meditate on the flame of a candle, or on the inner light at the centre of your forehead.

★ Know thyself: in this one sentence lie the solutions to all our sufferings and the secrets to all our desires ★

You can meditate on the idea of love, or wisdom, or immortality, or any other concept. Or you can meditate by simply being aware of your thoughts as they pass through your mind. There are sitting, standing, walking, laughing, crying, dancing and chanting meditations.

You can live every single moment of the day and night as meditation. And this is just for starters.

If you have not explored meditation, I urge you to consider it. Making meditation a regular part of your life will open you up to new and exciting possibilities for your inner growth.

If you do not know where to begin, start with one of the books on the subject such as *The Little Manual of Meditation* and branch out from there. Or connect with a teacher, or contact people who have had experience with meditation. If you start now, you will be amazed, when you look back six months or a year from now, at how far you have come and by how much your life has changed for the better. You will also see how subtly you have been guided through the inner maze.

Meditation provides a natural unfolding of the process of inner exploration. Some of the rewards are immediate. Others take time, often years, to achieve. There is no substitute for simply doing it, and seeing what the rewards are for you.

Create Joy in Your Life

We all have special moments in our lives. They are available to us in one degree or another every single day. We can find them in the smile of someone we love, or in the smile of someone we do not even know. We can find them in the hug of a child, in the presence of a friend, or the touch of a lover.

Think about the times in your life when you have been overcome with joy. It is in those moments that you were in love with yourself and everyone else. It was in those moments that you believed you could conquer the world. It is from that belief and that love that we can create our lives.

Think about the things that bring you joy, then make a point of connecting with as many of them as possible and as often as possible. Tap into moments of joy again and again, and absorb them into your present moment.

Slow Down

The speed of life on the fast track permeates every area of our lives. Hurrying becomes a habit. Even after we have simplified many of our daily routines, if we are still surrounded by fast moving people and telephones that never stop ringing, slowing down can take a major effort.

> We all have special moments in our lives. They are available to us in one degree or another every single day

Start by thinking how you can slow down your morning routine. Getting up even half-an-hour earlier, so that you do not have to rush out of the door, will make a big difference in the pace of your entire day. Take the time to sit down for your morning meal. Eat in a leisurely manner so you can feast on each bite. Eliminate the distractions of the radio, television and morning paper. Simply enjoy eating.

Make the gathering, preparation and consumption of food a conscious part of your inner quest, especially if you have lunch or dinner in fast-paced restaurants away from the peace and quiet you have established in your home. Plan to leave home early enough so you do not arrive at the office panting at the start of your work day. If you drive, make a point of staying within the posted speed limit. Learn to appreciate moving with purpose at a leisurely pace.

Place Post-it notes around your home or office to remind yourself to slow down. Over and over I have found that rushing through a project meant getting it wrong and losing time in the end by having to do it again, either partially or completely. Take your time and do it right in the first place, and enjoy the process as you go along. Always remember that life is the journey as well as the destination. Be with the moment and enjoy all that it brings. For, it is soon going to become your yesterday, it is already on its way to becoming a memory.

Make a concerted effort to examine all the areas of your life and figure out where you can slow down. If you have simplified a lot of your daily and weekly routines, you will not only have more time but can derive more pleasure from each thing you do throughout the day. Slowing down will help you keep in touch with how you feel about what you are doing and make it easier to connect with your inner self.

Ultimately, we have to be with our inner self. That is the treasure house that holds our source of joy. It has the key to happiness. Don't believe me? Try this simple exercise. Write down the five things or activities that bring you happiness. Let us say you have written 'visiting new restaurants' as one of the five. Okay, now ask yourself that if going to restaurants makes me happy, then if I go to seven restaurants in that many days, will I be over-the-moon happy? The honest answer would probably be 'No'. An excess of something you enjoy does not necessarily translate into happiness. I am, of course, referring to material, tangible things here.

> ★ Slowing down will help you keep in touch with how you feel about what you are doing and make it easier to connect with your inner self ★

Now, look at it this way. When you connect with your inner self, when you tap into the very origin of your being, you find a kind of joy that is almost difficult to explain. This is a state of spiritual well-being that goes beyond happiness. Here, you do not need riches or objects that make you happy. Here, you only need to be one with your Creator. Here, you are the universe; you are everywhere. You transcend time to find joy that is sublime. This is the kind of happiness that we were all made for. This is the happiness we all deserve.

Step 7

Choose sunshine over shadows

Whatever you focus on, grows

Simple Steps to a Joyful Life

Step 1

Choose happiness

A happy person is one who knows that there are options and always chooses the happy one

Step 2

Be happy anyway

A contented person is happy no matter how things are

Step 3

Accept imperfection

You don't have to wait for perfection to be happy

Step 4

Live in the present

This moment is your only reality

Step 5

Think happy thoughts

Negativity never enters a trained mind

Step 6

Be positive always, all-ways

Happiness is created within you, in your mind

Step 7

Choose sunshine over shadows

Whatever you focus on, grows

About the Author

Born and brought up in a business family in India, Vikas Malkani was the head of a large business enterprise when Awakening struck him at the age of 29. He has been called many things over the years: Spiritual Guru, Zen Master, Motivator, Mystic, Rich Monk, TV celebrity, Soul Coach and Reiki Master, to name a few. Other than that he is the founder of SoulCentre and a best-selling author.

Today, Vikas is considered one of the world's leading contemporary spiritual teachers. He teaches people to be successful in all aspects of life: the physical, emotional, mental and spiritual. His forte is to make the ancient wisdom of the spiritual Masters simple to understand and easy to apply to create a life of health, harmony and abundance on all levels.

Vikas is a disciple of Swami Rama of the Himalayas and has been trained in the wisdom lineage of the Himalayan Masters that involves the disciplines of meditation, spiritual wisdom

www.vikasmalkani.com
www.soulcentre.org

and yoga. A gifted orator, he is a keynote speaker at many international conferences and summits. He leads life-transforming workshops for adults and is also the creator of the SoulKids™ programme for children, which has made thousands of confident and creative children worldwide.

Vikas Malkani has been interviewed in many international newspapers and magazines and been a guest on numerous television and radio shows. His writings on self-awareness and spiritual wisdom appear regularly in magazines on yoga, holistic health and the spa industry. His television show airs on primetime every night on a national spiritual channel in India.

The Little Manual of Enlightenment

7 Valuable Tips for Those in Search of Awareness

Enlightenment is your birthright, let me show you how to arrive there, writes best-selling author Vikas Malkani in this book, *The Little Manual of Enlightenment*. These seven powerful tips take you to the world within and show you a whole new way of living. Learn how to live as a child of God, secure in the belief that the universe reflects you and your innermost thoughts. An essential guidebook for those in search of enlightenment.

Published by : Unicorn Books

The Little Manual of Success

9 Essential Secrets of Self-Made Millionaires

Best-selling author Vikas Malkani shares with us in this new book, *The Little Manual of Success*, the nine secrets that will lead us to success. These include taking responsibility for your acts, believing in yourself, rejecting mediocrity, following your heart and being persistent. These are the characteristics and qualities of super-achievers. This manual tells us that we, alone, will define what success means to us. It also teaches us to create a life of our choice.

Published by : Unicorn Books

The Little Manual of Meditation

15 Effective Ways to Discover Your Inner Self

Meditation is a very different, subtle and precise approach to locating your inner self, explains best-selling author Vikas Malkani in this book, *The Little Manual of Meditation*. He takes the reader through 15 steps that will bring positive results. Get ready to be freed from stress and enjoy a life of increased joy, clarity and awareness. Learn the simple techniques of meditation that will bring harmony to your life.

Published by : Unicorn Books